Look Around

Genesis 1 tells us how God created everything, even you.

bread   fish   elephant   moon   octopus   star

Find and circle the hidden pictures.

God created you in his image!

School Zone Publishing Company 12201

Bible Activities

Help Find the Inn

Follow the path to get help as the Good
Samaritan did in Luke 10:25–37.

Love your neighbor as yourself!

Bible Activities

Jesus Knows You

What does Jesus say we are to him in John 10:14?

Connect the dots • 1–10. Color the picture.

Jesus watches over you!

© School Zone Publishing Company 12201

Bible Activities

A Promise for All

God placed a reminder of his love in the
sky for everyone (Genesis 9:16).

Connect the dots ● A–J. Color ✏ the picture.

God's love for you stretches across the sky!

Dry Land Ahead

Genesis 8:6–12 tells us how Noah sent a dove to find dry land.

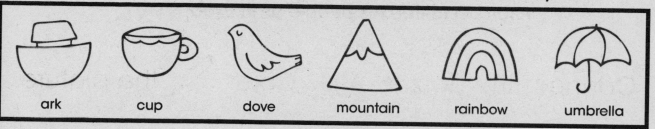

ark   cup   dove   mountain   rainbow   umbrella

Find and circle the hidden pictures.

God takes care of you and me!

School Zone Publishing Company 12201   Bible Activities

Help Find the Promised Land

Follow the path through the plagues God sent to
Pharaoh to free his people as in Exodus 9–11.

You are free to worship God!

A Promise Kept

Who was born to Abraham in Genesis 21
when he was very old?

Connect the dots • 1–10. Color the picture.

God keeps all of his promises!

Bible Activities

Jesus Is Missing

Jesus was a young boy when his
parents found him in the temple (Luke 2:41–49).

Connect the dots ● A–J. Color ✏ the picture.

Coat of Many Colors

Genesis 37:3 tells us how Joseph received a beautiful coat from his father.

Bible   chalice   coat   heart   pharaoh   shepherd's staff

Find and circle ✎ the hidden pictures.

Everyone is God's favorite!

Bible Activities

Help Thank Jesus

Follow the path to help the Leper thank
Jesus as told in Luke 17:12–19.

Thank Jesus for all he has done!

A New King

What was David anointed as
in 2 Samuel 2:4 by the men of Judah?

Connect the dots • 1–10. Color ✏ the picture.

4●   6●

2●   8●

3●   5●   7●

1☆ ●10   ●9

Jesus will give you a crown that will last forever!

Bible Activities

A Colorful Coat

Joseph's brothers were very angry about
his beautiful coat (Genesis 37:3 and 4).

Connect the dots • A–J. Color the picture.

Bible Activities © School Zone Publishing Company 12201

A Baby Brings Laughter

Genesis 21:1-7 tells us how happy Abraham and Sarah were when Isaac was born.

bottle   heart   rattle   rocking horse   shepherd's staff   star

Find and circle the hidden pictures.

God rejoiced the day you were born!

Bible Activities

Help Find Bethlehem

Follow the path to help Mary and Joseph find
a place to stay as in Luke 2:1–7.

There is room for everyone in God's kingdom.

Staying Faithful

Ruth stayed with Naomi. Boaz allowed
her to do this in Ruth 1 and 2.

Connect the dots ● 1–10. Color ✏ the picture.

Bible Activities

Armor of God

Be ready to stand firm in your faith
every day (Ephesians 6:10–18).

Connect the dots • A–J. Color ✏ the picture.

Baby in a Basket

Exodus 2:5-6 tells us how baby Moses was found.

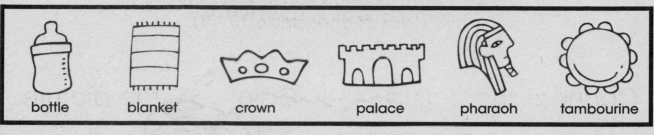

bottle   blanket   crown   palace   pharaoh   tambourine

Find and circle the hidden pictures.

God's love rescues you!

Bible Activities

Help Zacchaeus

Follow the path to help Zacchaeus be
with Jesus as in Luke 19:1–9.

Jesus wants to spend time with you!

18

Gold, Incense, and Myrrh

What did the Magi bring to Jesus in Matthew 2:11?

Connect the dots • 1–10. Color ✏ the picture.

You can bring Jesus gifts from your heart!

© School Zone Publishing Company 12201   Bible Activities

Follow That Star

The Wise Men knew how to find the
new baby king (Matthew 2:2).

Connect the dots ● A–J. Color ✎ the picture.

Bible Activities   © School Zone Publishing Company 12201

Crossing the Sea

Exodus 14:29–31 tells us how God led Moses across a sea.

| angel | chariot | donkey | fire | fish | tent |

Find and circle the hidden pictures.

God is with you wherever you go!

Bible Activities

Help the Children Get to Jesus

Follow the path to help the children get to Jesus as they did in Luke 18:16.

You are an important part of God's kingdom!

Shine Brightly
What does God in Psalm 18:28 turn your darkness into?

Connect the dots ● 1–15. Color the picture.

●15

●14

●11

3●

●10

13●

2●

12●

●9

7●

4●

8●

5●

6●

Bible Activities

A Drink of Water

A Samaritan woman was very surprised
to meet Jesus (John 4:7–9).

Connect the dots • A–J. Color the picture.

Jesus wants to be your friend!

Bible Activities

© School Zone Publishing Company 12201

Walls Tumbled Down

Joshua 6:1–20 tells us how Jericho tumbled to the ground.

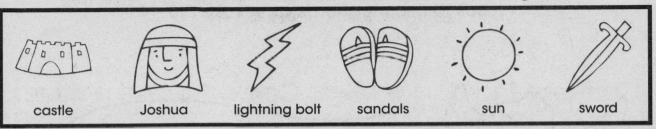

castle   Joshua   lightning bolt   sandals   sun   sword

Find and circle the hidden pictures.

God keeps his promises!

Bible Activities

Help Bring Good News

Follow the path to help the angel proclaim the birth of
Jesus to the shepherds as in Luke 2:8–14.

Proclaim the good news of God's love!

God's Word

What was written in Romans 15:4 to teach us
about God and give us hope?

Connect the dots • 1–15. Color the picture.

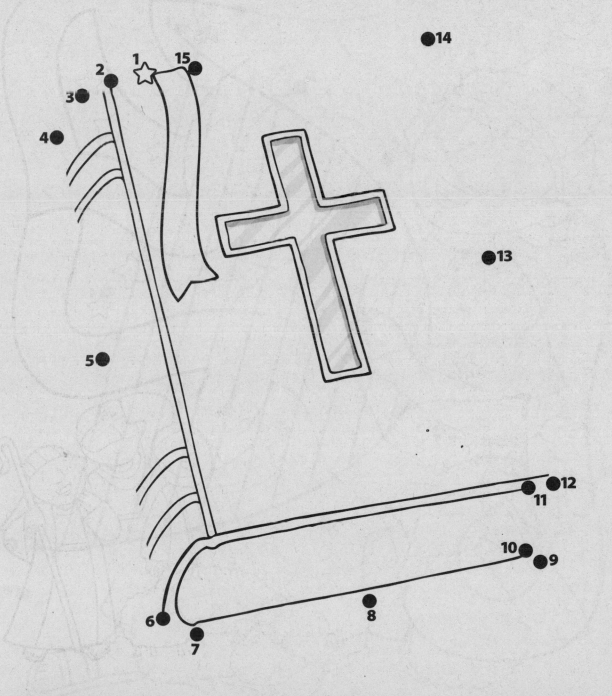

Bible Activities

Making Music

David loved praising the Lord with
his music (Psalm 33:2).

Connect the dots ● A–P. Color ✏ the picture.

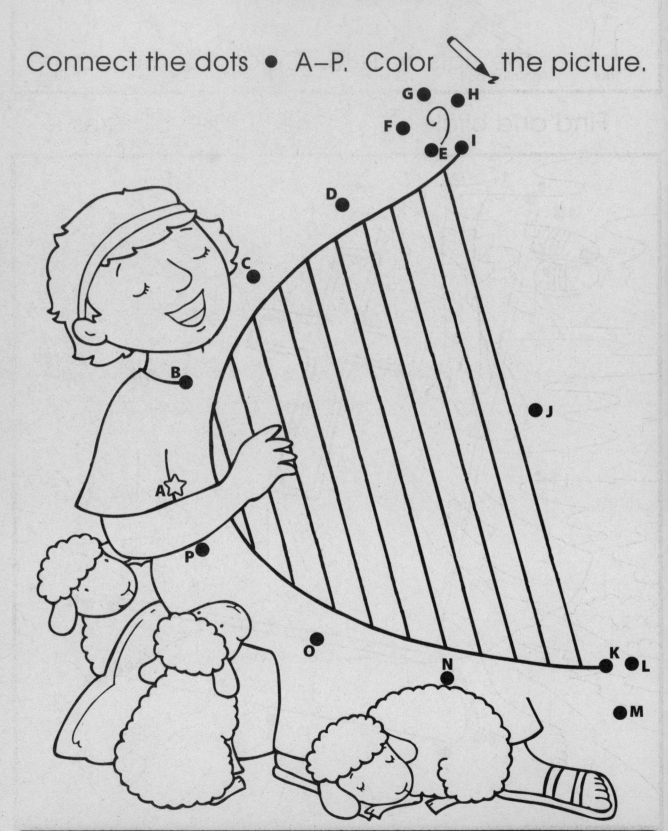

Tablets of Stone

Exodus 24:12 tells us how Moses received the Ten Commandments.

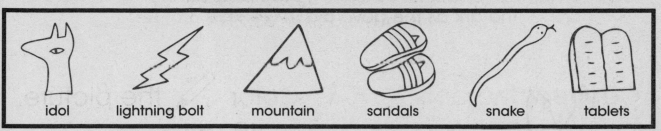

idol   lightning bolt   mountain   sandals   snake   tablets

Find and circle the hidden pictures.

Bible Activities

Help Find the Ark

Follow the waves to get the news of dry land to
the ark as the dove did in Genesis 8:6–12.

God takes care of you!

God's Special Helpers

Who will God command in Psalm 91:11 to
guard you in all of your ways?

Connect the dots • 1–15. Color 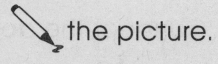 the picture.

Bible Activities

Super Strength

The Lord gave Samson strength one
last time (Judges 16:28–30).

Connect the dots • A–P. Color the picture.

Bible Activities

God Is Calling

1 Samuel 3:1–10 tells us how Samuel heard God call him three times.

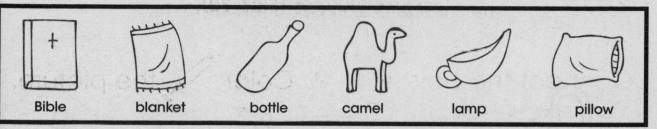

Bible   blanket   bottle   camel   lamp   pillow

Find and circle the hidden pictures.

God calls to you every day!

Bible Activities

Help Find the Lost Sheep

Follow the path to find the lost sheep as
the Shepherd did in Matthew 18:10–14.

You are one of God's beloved sheep!

Quite a Dream

What did Jacob see in a dream in Genesis 28:12
that reached all the way to heaven?

Connect the dots • 1–15. Color the picture.

School Zone Publishing Company 12201

The Spirit of God

The Holy Spirit comes to each
of us (Acts 2:1-4).

Connect the dots ● A–P. Color ✏️ the picture.

G● ●I

●H

●J

F● ●L

●K

D● ●E

●M

C●

B● ●N

A☆ ●O

P●

Best Friends

1 Samuel 18:1 tells us how David and Jonathan became friends.

Bible   flute   lamb   King Saul   shepherd's staff   tree

Find and circle the hidden pictures.

God gives you friends to love!

School Zone Publishing Company 12201   Bible Activities

Help Wear the New Coat

Follow the path through the coat Joseph received
from his father as in Genesis 37:3.

God wants you to wear the coat of his love!

One Hump or Two?

What in Mark 1:6 was John the Baptist's
coat made from?

Connect the dots • 1–15. Color the picture.

And It Was Good

God saw all he created and it
was good (Genesis 1:31).

Connect the dots • A–P. Color ✏ the picture.

Bible Activities   © School Zone Publishing Company 122

Esther Is Queen

Esther 2:17 tells us how Esther was crowned queen.

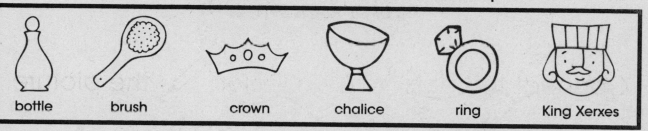

bottle   brush   crown   chalice   ring   King Xerxes

Find and circle the hidden pictures.

You will receive a crown in heaven!

Help the Raven Get to Elijah

Follow the path to help feed Elijah
as in 1 Kings 17:1-6.

Jesus is the bread of life!

Bible Activities © School Zone Publishing Company 1220

Going to Heaven
Who was taken up to heaven
in Luke 24:51?

Connect the dots • 1–15. Color 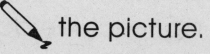 the picture.

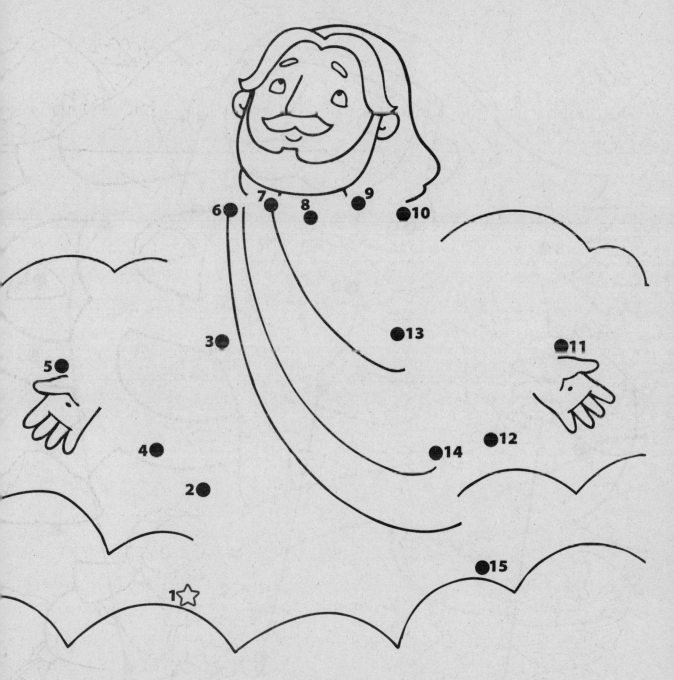

Moses on the Mountain

God called Moses to a mountaintop to
speak to him (Exodus 24:12).

Connect the dots • A–P. Color the picture.

Flames of Fire

Daniel 3 tells us what three men survived the fiery furnace.

chalice   fire   idol   king   praying hands   steak

Find and circle the hidden pictures.

Everyone is safe in God's love!

School Zone Publishing Company 12201   Bible Activities

Help the Snake Talk to Eve

Follow the snake to speak to Eve
as it did in Genesis 3:1–14.

King of All
What of Judah is Jesus called
in Revelation 5:5?

Connect the dots • 1–15. Color the picture.

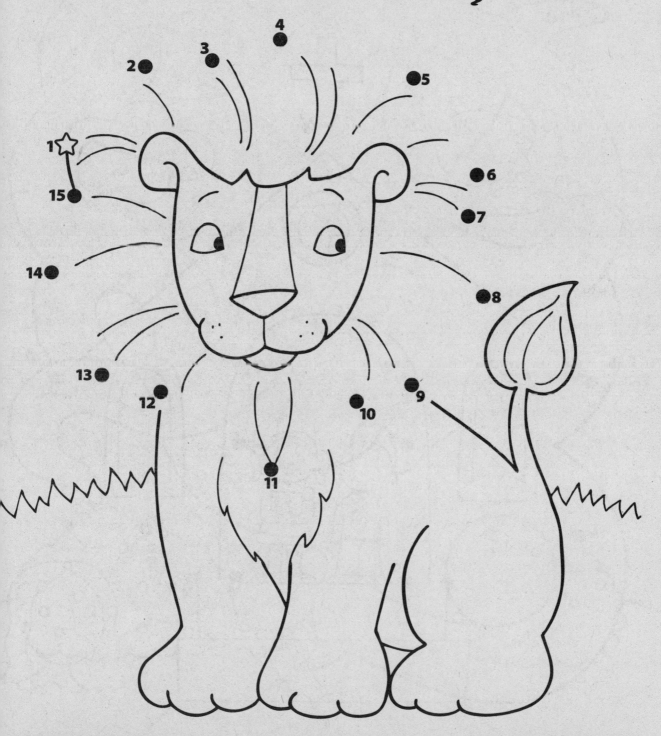

Jesus is the Lion of Judah—King of all!

chool Zone Publishing Company 12201

Bible Activities

God's House

We come together to worship and
praise God (Psalm 150).

Connect the dots • A–S. Color ✏️ the picture.

Bible Activities © School Zone Publishing Company 122

A Big Fish

Jonah 1–2:10 tells us what happened to Jonah.

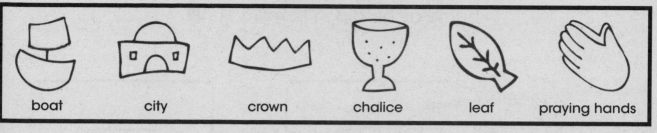

boat   city   crown   chalice   leaf   praying hands

Find and circle the hidden pictures.

God is with you wherever you are!

Bible Activities

Help the Son Get Home

Follow the path to help the son return
home as he did in Luke 15:11–32.

God waits for you with open arms!

The Third Day

What in Matthew 28:2 did an angel roll away at the tomb?

Connect the dots • 1–20. Color the picture.

19

20 18

2 16

1 17

3 15

4 5 12

13 14

6 11

7 10

8 9

Jesus rose from the dead to bring you new life!

Bible Activities

Feeding Lots of People

Jesus fed thousands of people and had
food left over (Mark 6:30-44).

Connect the dots ● A–S. Color 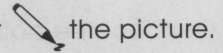 the picture.

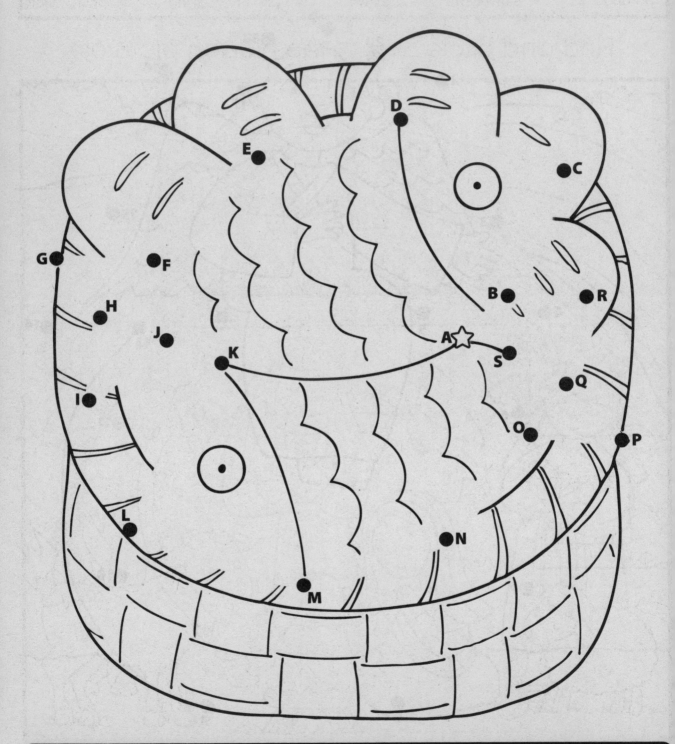

Bible Activities

Jesus Is Born

Luke 2:12 tells us where the shepherds found Jesus.

| angel | Bethlehem | crown | gift | king | shepherd's staff |

Find and circle the hidden pictures.

Help Solomon Receive Wisdom

Follow the path to the wisdom Solomon
prayed for in 1 Kings 3:9–12.

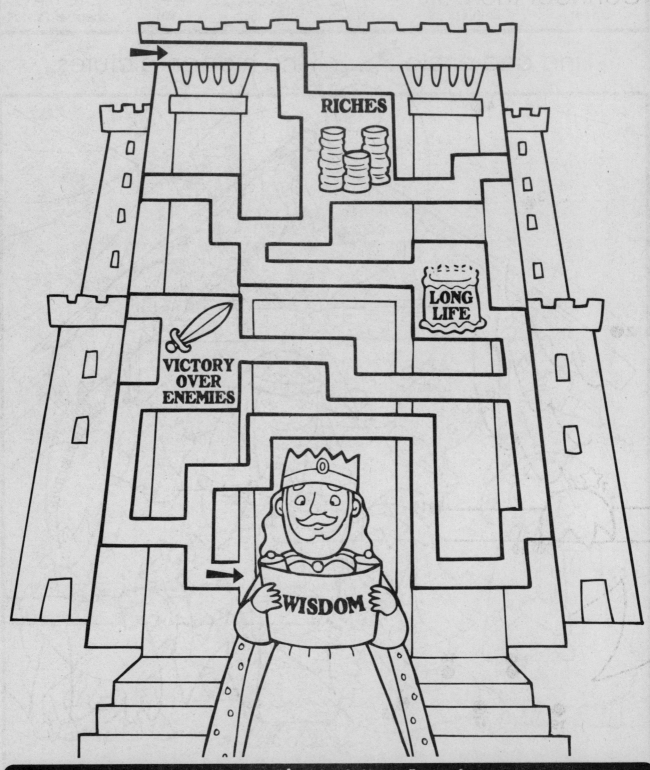

RICHES

LONG LIFE

VICTORY OVER ENEMIES

WISDOM

Pretty Birds

What is one of the beautiful birds God
created in Genesis 1:20?

Connect the dots • 1–20. Color the picture.

5
6
4
1
7
8
3
9
12
11
10
2
13
1
14
20
18
16
19
17
15

Alone in the Garden

Jesus talked to his father in the Garden
of Gethsemane (Mark 14:32).

Connect the dots • A–S. Color ✏ the picture.

you can talk to God whenever you want to!

Jesus in the Temple

Luke 2:46 tells us where Jesus was when his parents found him.

bread   sandals   scroll   sun   teacher   temple

Find and circle the hidden pictures.

You are never too young to share God's love!

    Bible Activities

Help Rescue Moses

Follow the path to find baby Moses as the
Pharaoh's daughter did in Exodus 2:5–10.

Bible Activities

© School Zone Publishing Company 1220

A Special Girl

What did Esther become in Esther 2:17 and 18
because she pleased the king?

Connect the dots • 1–20. Color the picture.

© School Zone Publishing Company 12201

A Boy and a Giant

David went into battle knowing God
was on his side (1 Samuel 17:37).

Connect the dots ● A–S. Color ✏ the picture.

Bible Activities   © School Zone Publishing Company   12201

Heaven Opened Up

Matthew 3:16–17 tells us how God spoke from heaven.

beehive　　bug　　cross　　dove　　horn　　heart

Find and circle the hidden pictures.

Jesus baptizes you with the Holy Spirit!

　　　　Bible Activities

Help Make David King

Follow the path to crown David king over the house of Judah as in 2 Samuel 2:1–7.

God's love is your crown!

A Talking Flame

What did Moses see in Exodus 3:2–4
when he heard God's voice?

Connect the dots • 1–20. Color the picture.

© School Zone Publishing Company 12201

Bible Activities

Blow That Trumpet

The priests obeyed God's command and
blew their trumpets (Joshua 6:8).

Connect the dots ● A–S. Color ✏ the picture.

I
J
●K

C
D G
H
L
●M P●
●Q

E
F
N
O

B●

●R

A
●S

Trust God to keep his promises!

Fishers of Men

Matthew 4:18-20 tells us how Jesus called his disciples.

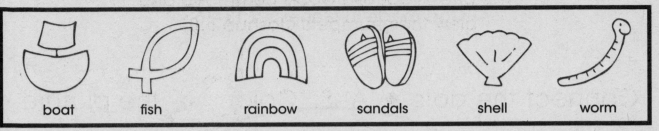

| boat | fish | rainbow | sandals | shell | worm |

Find and circle the hidden pictures.

You can be a disciple and follow Jesus!

Bible Activities

Complete the Rainbow

Follow the path to remind us of the promise
God made in Genesis 9:13–16.

Bible Activities

Divided Water

Who stretched out his hands as God commanded in Exodus 14
so the people could walk through the sea on dry land?

Connect the dots • 1–20. Color the picture.

God will keep you safe in his love!

Bible Activities

The Big Catch

The disciples were astonished when their
nets began to break (Luke 5:4–6).

Connect the dots ● A–S. Color ✏ the picture.

Through the Roof

Mark 2:1–12 tells us how a roof was opened to see Jesus.

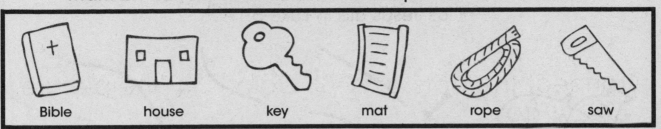

Bible   house   key   mat   rope   saw

Find and circle the hidden pictures.

Your faith can help a friend!

    Bible Activities

Help the Fish Reach the Net

Follow the waves to fill the net with fish as Jesus did in Luke 5:1–7.

Good News

Who did God send in Luke 2:1–13 to tell the shepherds about his son's birth?

Connect the dots • 1–20. Color the picture.

71

A Long Walk

Mary and Joseph made a very long
trip to Bethlehem (Luke 2:4 and 5).

Connect the dots • A–Z. Color ✏ the pict_____

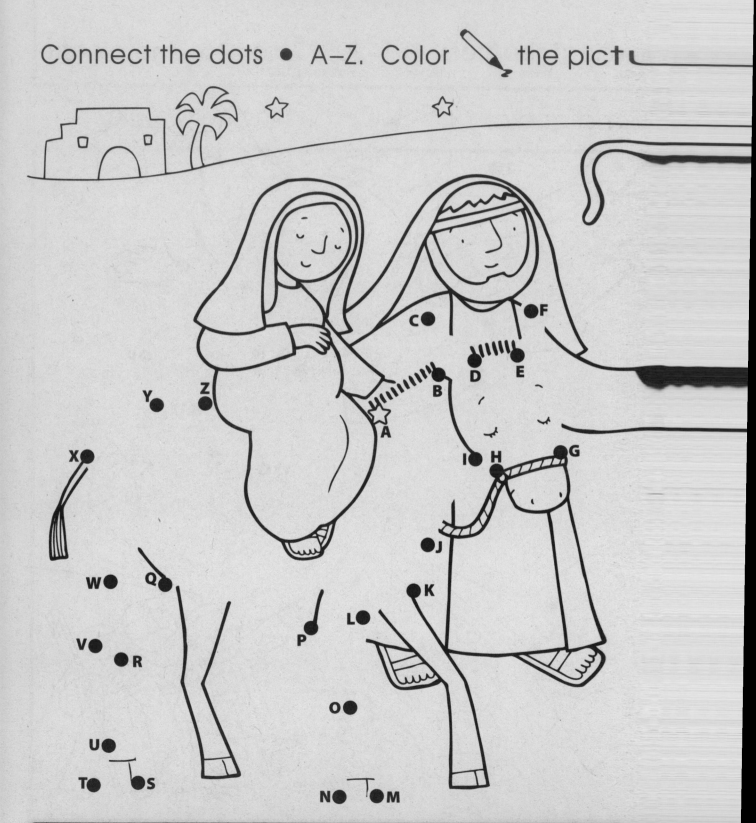

God is with you wherever you go!

Calming the Storm

Luke 8:22–25 tells us how a storm obeyed Jesus.

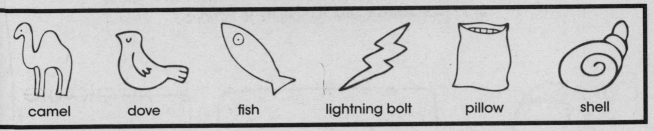

camel   dove   fish   lightning bolt   pillow   shell

Find and circle the hidden pictures.

Jesus is with you when you're afraid!

    Bible Activities

Help the Boy Get to His Basket

Follow the path to help feed 5,000 people
as Jesus did in John 6:9–11.

A False Idol

What did Aaron build in Exodus 32:1–8
that displeased God?

Connect the dots ● 1–20. Color ✏ the picture.

Bible Activities

A Special Chest

The Ten Commandments were placed in
a very special place (Exodus 25).

Connect the dots • A–Z. Color the picture.

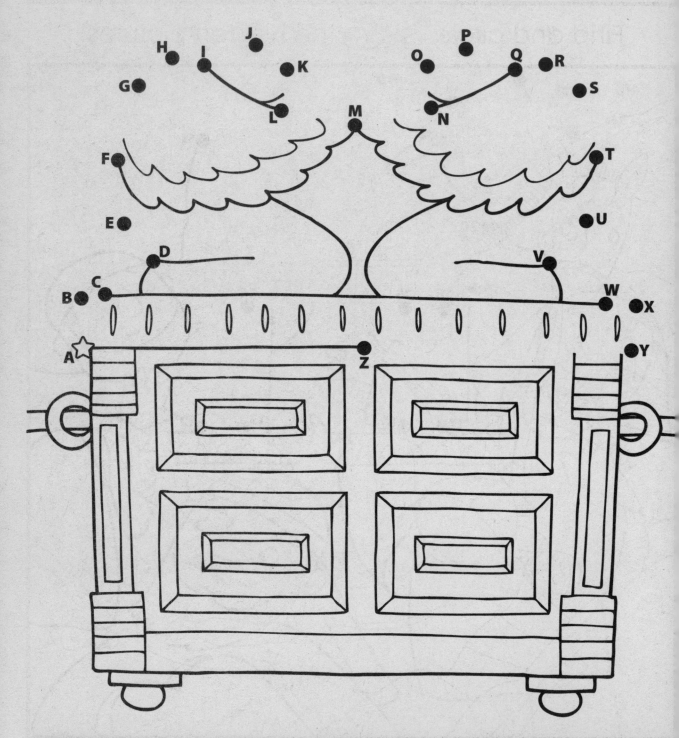

Left by the Road

Luke 10:25–37 tells us about a Good Samaritan who helped his neighbor.

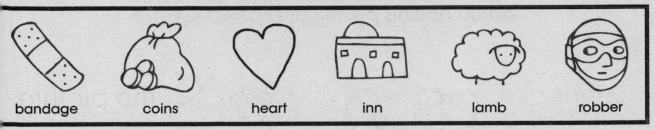

bandage coins heart inn lamb robber

Find and circle the hidden pictures.

Jesus wants you to help others!

School Zone Publishing Company 12201

Bible Activities

Help Crumble Walls

Follow the path around the city of Jericho as
Joshua and his people did in Joshua 6:1–5.

Bible Activities   © School Zone Publishing Company 12201

A New Creation

What is used to symbolize "the old has gone and the new has come" from 2 Corinthians 5:17?

Connect the dots • 1–25. Color the picture.

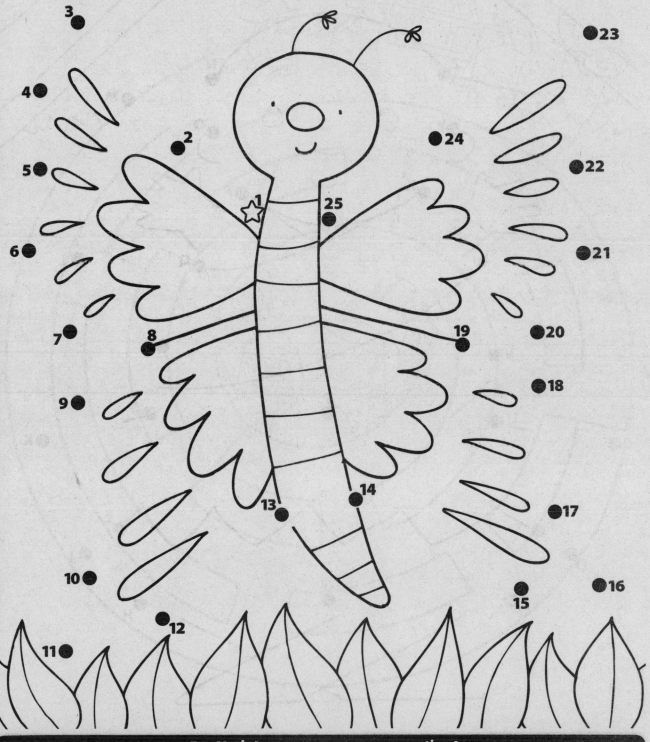

In Christ you are a new creation!

Bible Activities

A Baby King

Mary's baby came to earth to be
the Lord of all (Luke 2).

Connect the dots • A–Z. Color the picture.

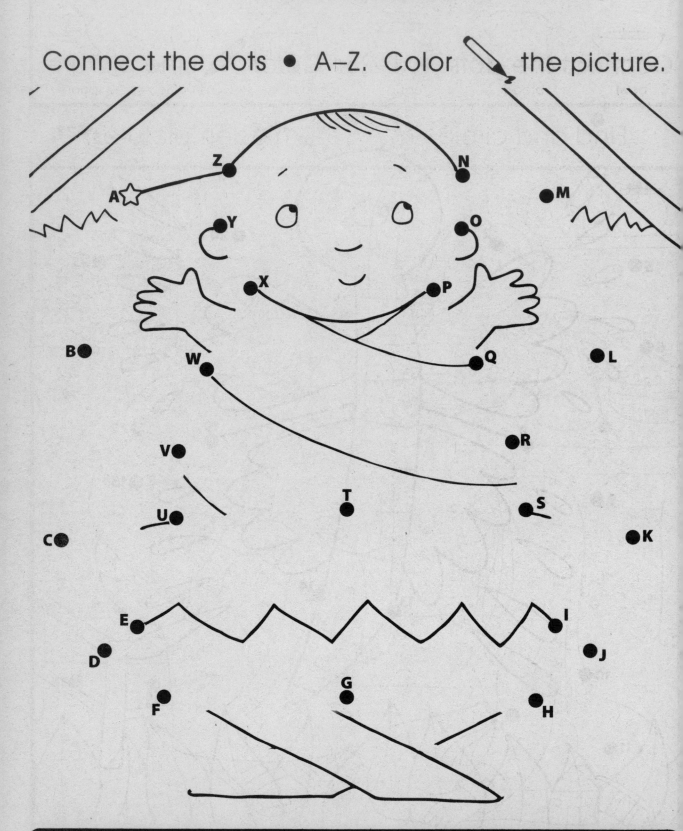

Bible Activities · © School Zone Publishing Company 12201

Jesus Visits His Friends

Luke 10:38–42 tells us what Jesus said to Mary and Martha.

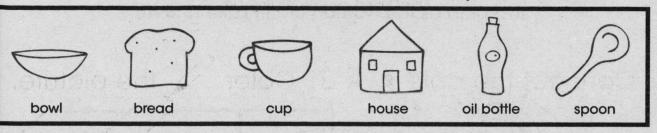

bowl   bread   cup   house   oil bottle   spoon

Find and circle the hidden pictures.

Take time for Jesus every day!

Bible Activities

Help Find the Coin

Follow the path through the house to find the
lost coin as the woman did in Luke 15:8–10.

Let Them Come

Who did Jesus call to him in Luke 18:16 because
the kingdom of God belongs to them?

Connect the dots • 1–25. Color the picture.

Jesus loves all the children of the world!

Bible Activities

Remembering God's Love

We remember Jesus' love through this
special meal (Luke 22:19 and 20).

Connect the dots ● A–Z. Color 🖍 the picture.

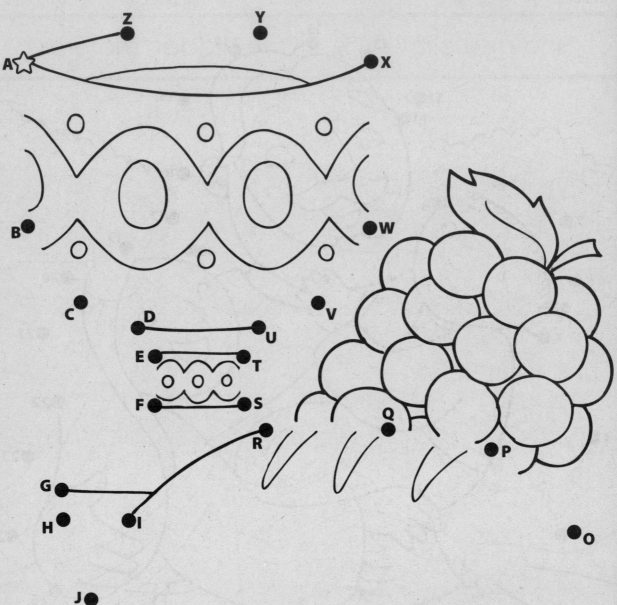

Remember Jesus' love for you!

Bible Activities © School Zone Publishing Company 122

Walking on Water

Matthew 14:25-31 tells us how Jesus walked on water.

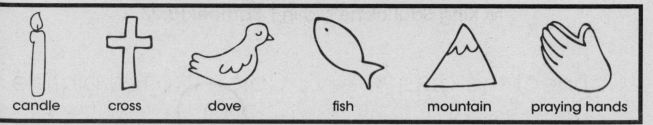

candle   cross   dove   fish   mountain   praying hands

Find and circle the hidden pictures.

Never doubt God's love for you!

Help David Play His Harp

Follow the path to help David play his soothing music
to King Saul as he did in 1 Samuel 16:23.

Be an instrument that sings of God's love!

Wonderful Riches

What did Jesus say in Matthew 13:44 the kingdom of heaven is like?

Connect the dots ● 1–25. Color ✏ the picture.

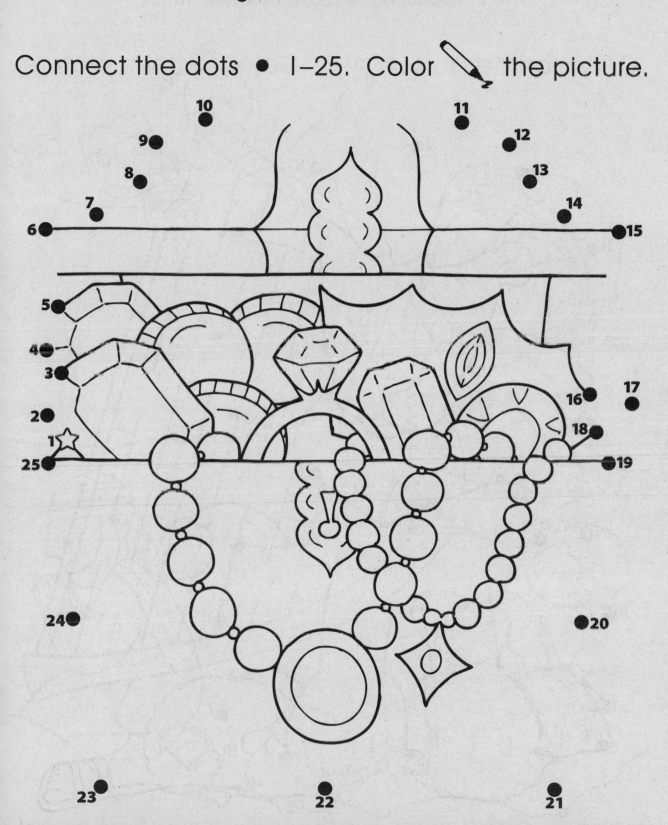

God's love for you is your treasure!

Bible Activities

A Quiet Lion

God kept Daniel safe all night
long (Daniel 6:16–23).

Connect the dots • A–Z. Color the picture.

God is with you all night long!

© School Zone Publishing Company 1220

Lost Coin Found

Luke 15:8-10 tells us how a woman searched her house for a lost coin.

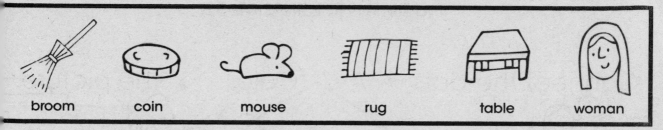

broom   coin   mouse   rug   table   woman

Find and circle the hidden pictures.

Jesus will find you wherever you are!

School Zone Publishing Company 12201   Bible Activities

Help Find Jesus

Follow the path to help Jesus' parents
find him as in Luke 2:41–52.

Talking to your friends about Jesus is fun!

Bible Activities

He Gave His All

What happened to Jesus in Luke 23:33
that took away your sins?

Connect the dots • 1–25. Color the picture.

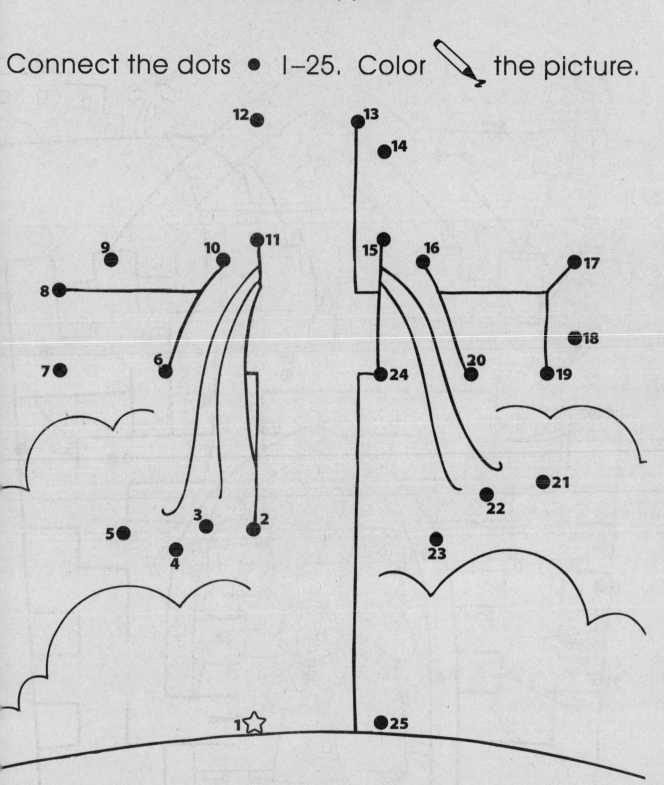

Take up your cross and follow Jesus!

Sign of the Spirit
The Holy Spirit descended onto Jesus
(Matthew 3:16).

Connect the dots • A–Z. Color the picture.

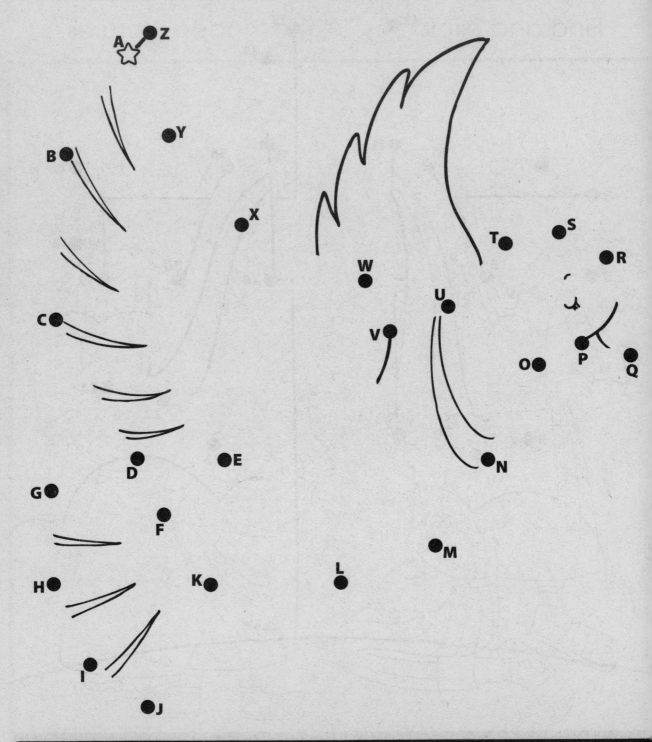

122

The Little Children

Mark 10:13–16 tells us what Jesus says about the kingdom of God.

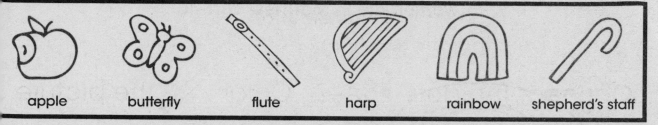

apple   butterfly   flute   harp   rainbow   shepherd's staff

Find and circle the hidden pictures.

Jesus loves you!

Help the Women Get to Jesus

Follow the path to the Risen Lord as the
women did in Matthew 28:1–10.

You are alive in Jesus!

Who Said That?

What did God use in Numbers 22:27-35
to speak to Balaam?

Connect the dots • 1–25. Color ✏ the picture.

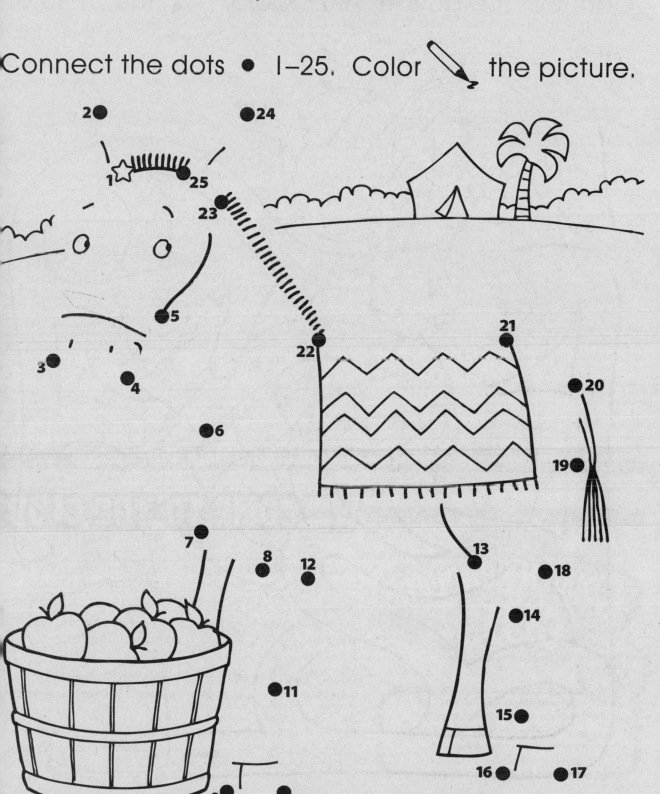

God's love is gentle and kind!

Talking to God

Jesus tells us how to pray (Matthew 6:9).

Connect the dots • A–Z. Color 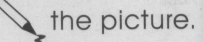 the picture.

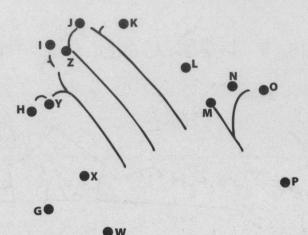

Praying is a special way to spend time with Jesus!

WELCOME TO THE CLUB

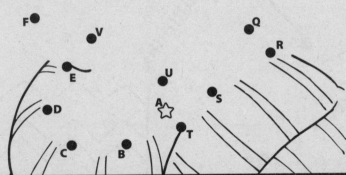

It's easy! Once you enter the redemption code, we'll e-mail you a link for your **free gift** of an original children's song.

When you register as a Golden Scholar Club member, you'll be eligible to receive special online coupons and you'll be updated on all of the great learning products that School Zone offers.

Have questions or need some help? You can call us at **1-616-846-9601** or e-mail us at **tech.support@schoolzone.com**

Shop your favorite retailer to discover more great School Zone products with exciting Golden Scholar Club gifts! Other free gifts include printable worksheets, interactive games, kid-friend videos, and read-along stories.

FREE GIFT

Register for your free gift!
Plus, receive special online coupons!
Visit: **www.schoolzone.com/club**
and enter your redemption code:
12201

Written by Linda Standke. **Illustrated by** Julie Anderson. **Edited by** Shannon M. Mullally, Ph.D.